The TRIUMPHS of HIS GRACE

Powerful piano settings of the hymns of Charles Wesley

Lloyd Larson

Editor: Larry Shackley
Music Engraving: Jeanette Dotson
Cover Design: Patti Jeffers

ISBN: 978-0-7877-1417-8

Lorenz

A Lorenz Company • www.lorenz.com

Foreword

Charles Wesley and his brother, John, are credited as the founders of the Methodist Church. Though they did not set out to establish a church movement, the impact of these two evangelists in their native England and later in colonial America cannot be overstated. But their influence extends far beyond the founding of the Methodist Church. Their hymn lyrics, particularly those of Charles Wesley, have shaped the singing faith of Christians across denominational lines since the earliest years of their ministry dating back to the mid-1700s.

The hymn lyrics of Charles Wesley are embraced as universal statements of praise and theological truths by Christians around the globe:

O for a thousand tongues to sing my great Redeemer's praise…

Come, Thou long-expected Jesus, born to set Thy people free…

Hark! the herald angels sing, "Glory to the newborn King…

Love divine, all loves excelling, Joy of heaven to earth come down…

Amazing love! How can it be that Thou, my God shouldst die for me?

Jesus, Lover of my soul, let me to Thy bosom fly….

Christ the Lord is risen today, Alleluia!

Praise the Lord who reigns above and keeps His court below….

These foundational truths and expressions of faith have been wed to memorable melodies and indelibly etched on the minds and hearts of believers for generations. They have solidified our theology and shaped our understanding of the eternal God. In playing these hymns, it is impossible for me to exclude the lyrics in my mind from these timeless melodies. I pray that you will find renewed inspiration in these enduring hymns and unchanging truths which are inherent in the lyrics of Charles Wesley.

– Lloyd Larson

Contents

4

Praise the Lord Who Reigns Above

Praise the Lord who reigns above and keeps His court below;
Praise the holy God of love, and all His greatness show;
Praise Him for His noble deeds, praise Him for His matchless power;
Him from whom all good proceeds let earth and heaven adore.

Lloyd Larson
Tune: AMSTERDAM
from *Foundery Collection*, 1742

Duration: 2:30

www.lorenz.com

JD

And Can It Be That I Should Gain?

And can it be that I should gain an interest in the Savior's blood?
Died He for me, who caused His pain? For me, who Him to death pursued?
Amazing love! how can it be that Thou, my God, shouldst die for me?
Amazing love! how can it be that Thou, my God, shouldst die for me?

Lloyd Larson
Tune: SAGINA
by **Thomas Campbell**, 1825

Duration: 3:15

JD

12

Love Divine, All Loves Excelling

Love divine, all loves excelling, Joy of heaven to earth come down,
Fix in us Thy humble dwelling, all Thy faithful mercies crown.
Jesus, Thou art all compassion, pure, unbounded love Thou art;
Visit us with Thy salvation, enter every trembling heart.

Lloyd Larson
Tune: BEECHER
by **John Zundel**, 1870

Duration: 3:10

Come, Thou Long-Expected Jesus

Come, Thou long-expected Jesus, born to set Thy people free;
From our fears and sins release us; let us find our rest in Thee.
Israel's strength and consolation, hope of all the earth Thou art;
Dear Desire of every nation, Joy of every longing heart.

Lloyd Larson
Tune: HYFRYDOL
by **Rowland H. Prichard**, ca. 1830

Joyously, steadily ♩ = ca. 144

Duration: 2:45

JD

20

70/1944L-20

Hark! the Herald Angels Sing

Hark! the herald angels sing, "Glory to the newborn King;
Peace on earth, and mercy mild, God and sinners reconciled!"
Joyful, all ye nations, rise, join the triumph of the skies;
With th'angelic host proclaim, "Christ is born in Bethlehem!"
Hark! the herald angels sing, "Glory to the newborn King."

Lloyd Larson
Tune: MENDELSSOHN
by **Felix Mendelssohn**, 1840

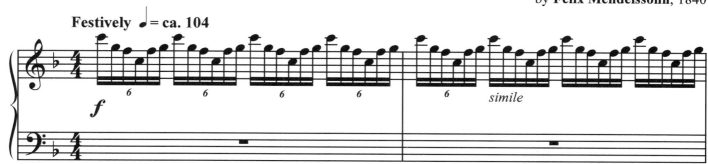

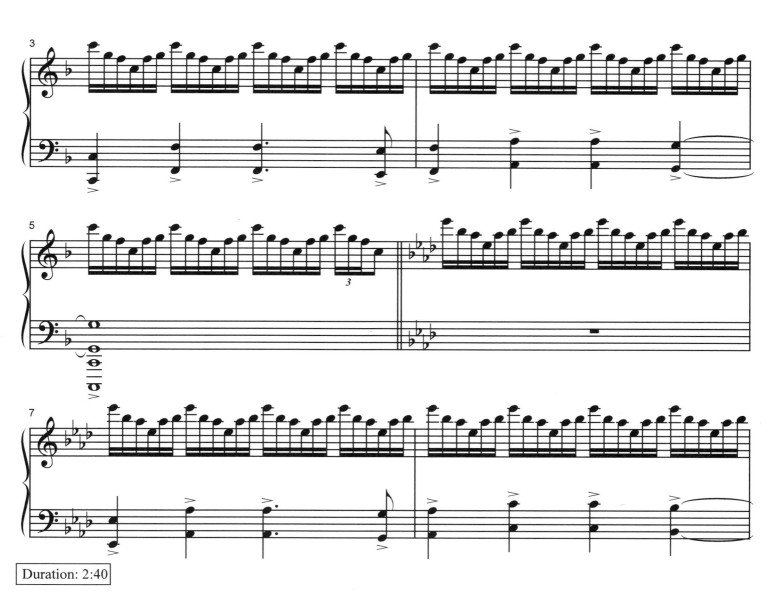

Duration: 2:40

JD

24

70/1944L-24

Jesus, Lover of My Soul

Jesus, Lover of my soul, let me to Thy bosom fly,
While the nearer waters roll, while the tempest still is high;
Hide me, O my Savior, hide till the storm of life is past;
Safe into the haven guide; O receive my soul at last!

Lloyd Larson
Tune: ABERYSTWYTH
by **Joseph Parry**, 1879

Duration: 3:15

32

70/1944L-32

Christ the Lord Is Risen Today

Christ the Lord is risen today, Alleluia!
All creation, join to say Alleluia!
Raise your joys and triumphs high, Alleluia!
Sing, ye heavens, and earth reply, Alleluia!

Lloyd Larson
Tune: EASTER HYMN
from *Lyra Davidica*, London, 1708

Duration: 3:00

JD

34

Triumphantly ♩ = ca. 96

此处无效

36

O for a Thousand Tongues to Sing

O for a thousand tongues to sing my great Redeemer's praise,
The glories of my God and King, the triumphs of His grace.
My gracious Master and my God, assist me to proclaim,
To spread through all the earth abroad the honors of Thy name.

Lloyd Larson
Tune: AZMON
by **Carl G. Glaser**, 1828

Duration: 1:30

JD